Kipper
Gets Nits!

Written by Roderick Hunt and Annemarie Young

Illustrated by Alex Brychta

OXFORD
UNIVERSITY PRESS

Kipper was in the garden with Dad,
Biff and Chip. They were watering
their sunflowers. Mum was going to
give a prize for the tallest sunflower.

"Dad's sunflower is winning, but only just," said Biff. "Mum is going to judge them in two weeks, so we've got time to catch up."

"Kipper keeps scratching his neck," said Chip. "I think he must have fleas."

"It can't be fleas," said Dad.

"But you might have head lice,"
said Mum. "Try not to scratch."

"Ergh!" said Biff. "That's
horrible."

"It's not so horrible," said Mum.
"I had head lice when I was a little
girl. It doesn't mean you're dirty.
Let me have a look."

"Hmm," said Mum. "I think I can see some lice and nits. But I'll have to go to the chemist and get a louse comb to make sure."

"If it is head lice we'll have to tell the school," said Mum.

"Sorry!" said Dad, "I forgot. The school sent this letter about nits."

The chemist showed Mum a special kit to get rid of lice. "This is a bug buster kit," he said. "Don't forget to check the whole family."

"We'll have to do some bug
busting!" said Mum.

Dad washed the children's hair
and put conditioner on it.

Then Mum combed it. Biff didn't have any lice in her hair. But Chip and Kipper did, and the combing got rid of the lice.

Mum plaited Biff's hair tightly to keep it out of the way.

"Now I want to see how your sunflowers are doing," said Mum.

"They're all quite tall," said
Mum.

"But Dad is winning," said Kipper.

"There's still time!" said Mum.

The next day, Kipper got up
early. He got the watering can and
the plant food and went out to his
sunflower. Floppy came out to help.

Kipper put the plant food into the
water and gave it to his sunflower.
"This should do the trick," he said.

Floppy wagged his tail.

A few days later, after the bug
busting, Chip put plant food into
the watering can and went out to
his sunflower.

He watered his sunflower with the
plant food. "This should do the
trick," he said.

Floppy wagged his tail.

Later that week, Biff got up early.
She watered her sunflower with
plant food. "That should do it,"
she said.

Later, Dad went to check his
sunflower. It was taller than the
others, but snails had eaten the
leaves, and the head was droopy!

After two weeks, Mum checked the children's hair.

"Hooray!" she said. "You're all clear of lice and nits."

"Now let's go and check the sunflowers," said Dad.

"I wonder if Dad's is still the tallest?" said Biff.

Dad's sunflower looked twice as
tall as the others.

"Aren't I a genius?" asked Dad.

"Oh Dad!" laughed Biff.

"It needed a helping hand," said Dad, "after the snails attacked it."

"That's cheating," said Mum. "No prize for you!"

Mum started measuring the other
sunflowers. Floppy started scratching.
"Has he got nits, too?" asked Biff.
"Not nits," said Dad. "Fleas!"

Talk about the story

Why did Mum say getting nits wasn't horrible?

Why do you think Mum wanted to tell the school about Kipper's nits?

How did Mum and Dad get rid of the head lice?

What would you do if you thought you had head lice?

Life cycle of the head louse

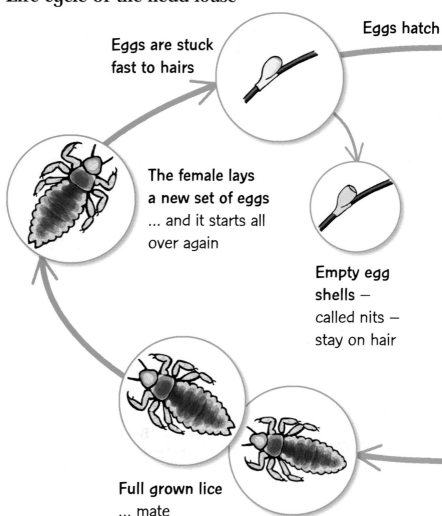

Eggs are stuck fast to hairs

Eggs hatch

The female lays a new set of eggs ... and it starts all over again

Empty egg shells — called nits — stay on hair

Full grown lice ... mate

Louse nymph
— stage 1

Louse nymph
— stage 2

Louse nymph
— stage 3

Bug Buster Kit

The Bug Buster Kit is available from
Community Hygiene Concern

Website: www.chc.org

Helpline: +44 (0)1908 561928

CHC Reg. Charity No: 801371

29

Spot the pair

Find the two sunflowers that are exactly the same.